INDIANA
Macmillan/McGraw-Hill **TIMELINKS**

Indiana in the Nation and the World

Student Practice and Activity Workbook

D1270841

 Macmillan/McGraw-Hill

The *McGraw·Hill* Companies

 **Macmillan
McGraw-Hill**

Send all inquiries to:
Macmillan/McGraw-Hill
8787 Orion Place
Columbus, OH 43240-4027

ISBN: 978-0-02-151814-2
MHID: 0-02-151814-9

Printed in the United States of America.

2 3 4 5 6 7 8 9 10 021 13 12 11 10 09

Grade 4 Workbook
Table of Contents

Unit 1

Unit 2

Unit 3

Unit 4

Unit 5

Unit 6

Name _____ Date _____

CURRICULUM CONNECTION ⟩ ART

CURRICULUM CONNECTION ⟩ LANGUAGE ARTS

Landform Postcard

Choose a landform found in Indiana and draw it on the postcard below. Create a title for your postcard. Include a caption under your drawing that identifies the region where the landform is often found.

Title _____

Plot a Trip

Use the map to plan a trip around the three regions of Indiana. Estimate the latitude and longitude of each of your stops.

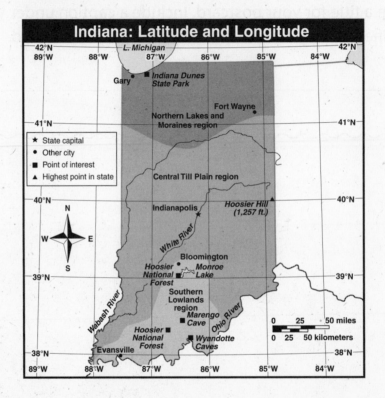

Indiana: Latitude and Longitude

Day 1

Indiana Dunes State Park

_____

Day 2

Indianapolis

_____

Day 3

Indiana's highest point

_____

Day 4

Hoosier National Forest

_____

Day 5

Marengo Cave

_____

Day 6

Wyandotte Cave

_____

Tornado Alley Map

Create your own map of Tornado Alley. Look at the list of states that some researchers say form Tornado Alley. Color the states on the map.

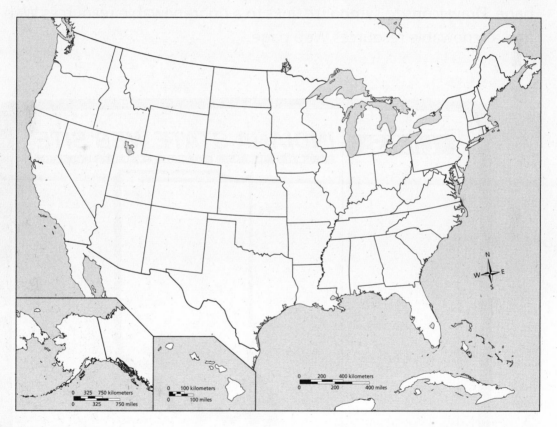

Arkansas	Kentucky (western part)	Oklahoma
Colorado (eastern part)	Louisiana	South Dakota
Illinois	Missouri	Tennessee (western part)
Indiana	North Dakota	Texas
Iowa	Nebraska	Wyoming (eastern part)
Kansas	Ohio (western part)	

Name _____   Date _____

Indiana Resources Web Site

Design a Web page about Indiana's natural resources. Include a name for your Web page. Write a sentence telling visitors the purpose of the Web page. Draw icons to symbolize links to a nonrenewable resources Web page and a renewable resources Web page.

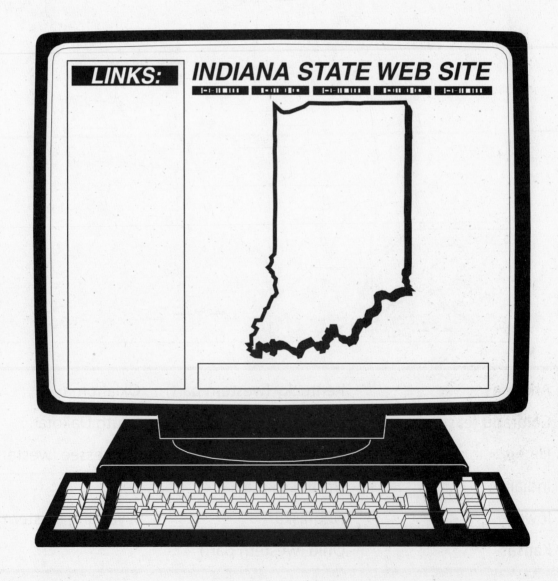

Name _____ Date _____

CURRICULUM CONNECTION | LANGUAGE ARTS

Water Usage Graph

Indiana's water has many different uses. Look at the circle graph and answer the questions.

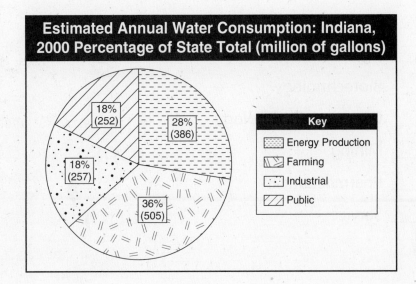

Estimated Annual Water Consumption: Indiana, 2000 Percentage of State Total (million of gallons)

18% (252)
28% (386)
18% (257)
36% (505)

Key
- Energy Production
- Farming
- Industrial
- Public

1. What does the circle graph show? _____

2. Which group uses the most water? _____

3. Which group uses the least water? _____

_____

4. Predict how water usage might change in the future. Explain your

answer. _____

_____

Rate Indiana Industries

Indiana has many industries. Look at the list below. Which industry interests you the most? Which industry interests you the least? Rate the industries from 1 to 6. Then answer the questions.

_____ Agriculture

_____ Biotechnology

_____ Computer Technology

_____ Mining

_____ Pharmaceutical

_____ Service

1. Which industry interests you the most? Why? _____

_____

2. Which industry interests you the least? Why? _____

_____

Hall of Fame

Indiana has many famous athletes, artists, entertainers, and writers. Nominate your favorite Hoosier for a new Indiana Hall of Fame. Fill out the form below.

NOMINATION FORM FOR INDIANA HALL OF FAME

Date:

Person nominated:

Field of Work:

Reason for Nomination:

Signed:

Vocabulary Review

Look at the words in the box below. Write the letter of each word on the line next to its definition.

a. equator	**d.** tornado	**g.** manufacturing
b. moraine	**e.** limestone	**h.** graph
c. productivity	**f.** immigrant	

_____ **1.** a soft rock that is used to make roadways and buildings

_____ **2.** a wind shaped like a funnel that moves quickly over ground

_____ **3.** a line of low hills formed by rocks that were pushed up by glaciers

_____ **4.** an imaginary line halfway between the North and South Poles

_____ **5.** the amount of goods or services made in a period of time

_____ **6.** a person who moves to a new country to live

_____ **7.** a diagram that shows information in a visual way

_____ **8.** the making of goods by machinery

Archaeology Report

Look at the items that archaeologists have uncovered in Indiana. Think about what these objects tell you about how people lived thousands of years ago. Study each item. Think about its use. Then write your report.

spear point

axe blade

shell from the Gulf of Mexico

Artifact Conclusions

Item:

Conclusion:

Item:

Conclusion:

Item:

Conclusion:

Mysteries of the Mounds DVD

Create a DVD case for a new movie about Native American mounds in Indiana. Design a cover for your case. On the back of the case, write a description of your film.

Front

Back

CURRICULUM CONNECTION > READING

CURRICULUM CONNECTION > LANGUAGE ARTS

Story of The Three Sisters

There are many Native American stories about the three sisters. The sisters stand for three plants that are always grown together and eaten together. Here is one story. Read the story. Then use the picture to help you answer the questions.

There were three sisters who always wanted to be together. The oldest sister was tall and stood very straight. The middle sister climbed on the eldest. The youngest sister crawled on the ground.

1. Which plant do you think was the oldest sister? Why?

_____

_____

2. Which plant do you think was the middle sister? Why?

_____

_____

3. Which plant do you think was the youngest sister? Why?

_____

_____

Use with Unit 2, Chart and Graph Skills

Studying a Wigwam

Look at the cutaway diagram of the wigwam below. Then answer the questions.

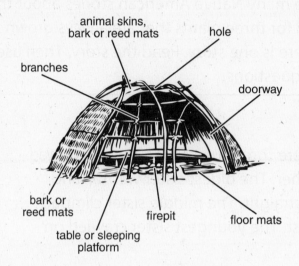

animal skins, bark or reed mats

hole

branches

doorway

bark or reed mats

firepit

floor mats

table or sleeping platform

1. What holds up the wigwam?

_____

2. What things can you find on the outside of the wigwam?

_____

3. What things can you find inside the wigwam?

_____

4. What things can a cutaway diagram of a wigwam show you that a photograph of the outside of wigwam cannot?

_____

_____

La Salle's Journal

The map shows La Salle's route in his search to find the Northwest Passage to the sea. Imagine that you are La Salle and have just traveled across the Great Lakes. Write a journal entry about the day that you finally arrived in Indiana.

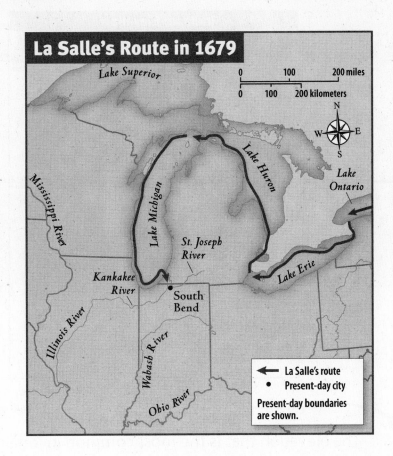

La Salle's Route in 1679

_____

_____

_____

_____

Name _____ Date _____

Looking at Elevation

Look at the elevation map of Indiana and use it to complete the paragraphs below.

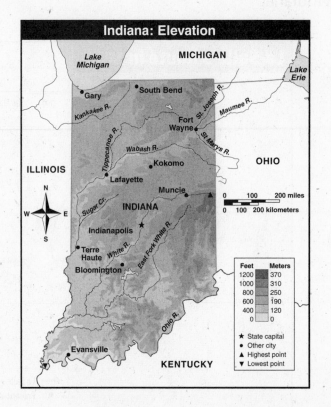

The elevation that is the most common in Indiana is
_____. The central eastern part of the state has an
elevation of _____. The southwest part of the state's
elevation is _____.

Of the cities shown, _____ has the lowest elevation.
The city of _____ is near the area with the highest
elevation. The elevation range of Indiana's capital city is
_____ feet.

Fur Advertisement

Fur trappers who came to America sold their furs to people in Europe. Create an advertisement for an item made out of beaver fur or raccoon fur. Draw a picture of your item. Then describe your item to convince people to buy it. Make sure to state in your ad that the fur comes from America.

Name _____ Date _____

Proclamation Debate

People argued about the Proclamation of 1763. This announcement by Great Britain said that colonists could not settle on land west of the Appalachian Mountains. This land was set aside for Native Americans. Write a debate about the issue between a British official, an American colonist, and a Native American. Think about their different points of views.

Three Viewpoints

British Official	Colonist	Native American

A Soldier's Letter

George Rogers Clark and his soldiers had a difficult journey to Fort Sackville. Reread about the march to Fort Sackville on page 83 of your textbook. Imagine that you are one of the soldiers on Clark's march. Write a letter to a friend or relative telling about your journey.

Vocabulary Review

Next to each definition below is the first letter of the word that matches it. Try to use your memory to fill in the rest of each word! If you get stuck, look for the words in Unit 2 of your textbook.

1. a _ _ _ _ _ _ _   the remains of objects made or used by people in the past

2. m _ _ _ _   a hill or ridge of earth

3. a _ _ _ _ _ _ _   an agreement between two or more groups to work together in doing something

4. c _ _ _ _ _   a country or region that is ruled by another country

5. e _ _ _ _ _ _ _ _   the height of the land above sea level

6. m _ _ _ _ _ _ _ _ _   someone who teaches others about his or her religion

7. r _ _ _ _ _ _ _ _   an armed fight against a government

8. f _ _ _ _ _ _ _   the land at the edge of a settled area

Make a Treaty

Create your own Treaty of Greenville. Fill in the information below. Then sign the treaty.

The Treaty of Greenville

This treaty is important because _____

_____

_____

Native Americans shall give up _____

_____

Native Americans shall receive:

1. _____

2. _____

Signed:

_____

Name _____ Date _____

CURRICULUM CONNECTION LANGUAGE ARTS

CURRICULUM CONNECTION MATH

Little Turtle Time Line

Create a time line that shows events in Little Turtle's life. Put the dates and events on the time line in the order that they happened. Then answer the questions.

1752   born in what is now Indiana

1790   becomes a leader of the Miami group

1795   signs the Treaty of Greenville

1812   dies in what is now Fort Wayne, Indiana

Little Turtle's Life

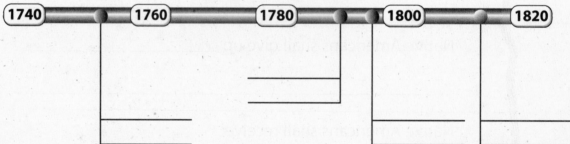

1. What event happened in 1790?

_____

2. Did Little Turtle become a leader of the Miami group before or after signing the Treaty of Greenville?

_____

Name _____   Date _____

From Territory to State

Look at the map and map titles below. Circle the correct title of the map. Then answer the question.

Indiana Territory: 1800   Indiana Territory: 1809

1. Explain why you chose the map title.

_____

_____

_____

_____

_____

1810 Cartoon

Newspapers often show cartoons about things that happen. Draw a cartoon for a newspaper in 1810. Show Tecumseh and Governor Harrison meeting at Vincennes. Write a sentence showing what they say to each other at the meeting in the speech balloons. Then answer the questions.

_____

1. Why did Tecumseh think the treaties that forced Native Americans to give up land were not fair?

_____

2. Why do you think that Governor Harrison did not agree with Tecumseh?

_____

Use with Unit 3, Map and Globe Skills

CURRICULUM CONNECTION ⟩ LANGUAGE ARTS

CURRICULUM CONNECTION ⟩ MATH

Compare Maps

Look at the two maps. Then answer the questions.

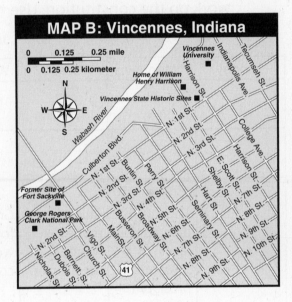

1. Which map has a map scale that shows a larger distance?

_____

2. Which map would be more useful to use if you wanted to walk around Vincennes? Why?

_____

_____

CURRICULUM CONNECTION ❯ **LANGUAGE ARTS**

CURRICULUM CONNECTION ❯ **MATH**

Statehood Calendar

The calendar events show what Indiana's 43 delegates did at Corydon to write a constitution. The arrows show the days that delegates continued to work on the constitution. Use the calendar to answer the questions below.

June 1816

Sunday	Monday	Tuesday	Wednesday	Thursday	Friday	Saturday
						1
2	3	4	5	6	7	8
9	10 The delegates elect Jennings president of the meeting.	11 Rules are made for the meeting.	12 Groups form to work on the constitution.	13 Groups report and vote on their findings. →	14	15 →
16	17 →	18 →	19 →	20 →	21 →	22 →
23	24 →	25 →	26 →	27 →	28 →	29 The meeting ends.
30						

1. On what date did the delegates first meet? _____

2. On which day of the week did the delegates not work? _____

3. For how many days did the delegates meet? _____

Pioneer To-Do List

Look at the list of things that pioneers needed to do when they arrived in Indiana. Number the items on the list in the correct order from 1 to 6. Then answer the questions.

_____ Cut down trees for the log cabin.

_____ Buy land under the Land Ordinance of 1785.

_____ Stack the logs to form walls for the log cabin.

_____ Gather tree branches and twigs for a lean-to.

_____ Fill the spaces between the logs of the log cabin with mud and clay.

_____ Build a lean-to.

1. A lean-to had only three walls. What kind of problems might this cause?

_____

_____

2. What do you think it would be like to live in one-room log cabin with eight family members? What would be difficult about it? What would be good about it?

_____

_____

_____

Name _____ Date _____

Historical Sign

Make a historical sign about New Harmony, Indiana. Make sure the sign tells visitors about the history of New Harmony.

History of Transportation Museum

Create exhibits for a History of Transportation Museum. Draw an example of each kind of transportation. Write about each type of transportation on the museum signs.

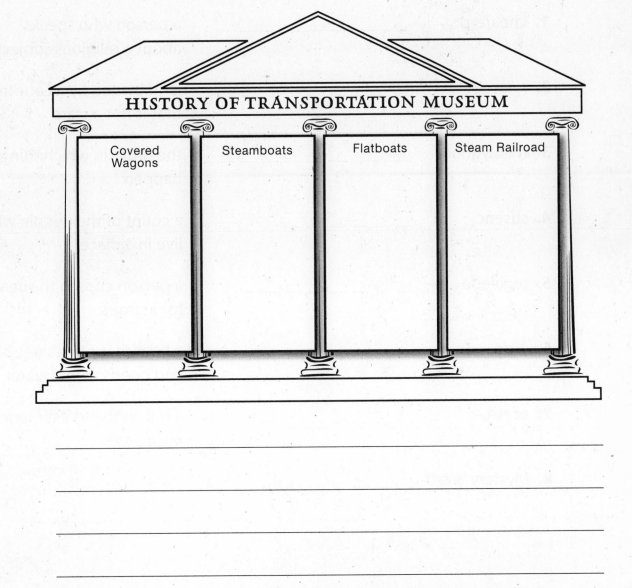

HISTORY OF TRANSPORTATION MUSEUM

Covered Wagons | Steamboats | Flatboats | Steam Railroad

Vocabulary Review

Use the definitions to help you figure out each scrambled word. Then place the numbered letters on the correct spaces at the bottom of the page to discover the mystery word.

Definition

1. chearerp   _ _ _ _ _ _ _ _   a person who speaks
                   1   about a religious subject

2. ryteroirt   _ _ _ _ _ _ _ _ _   land owned by a country
                        2   that is not a state

3. rhcolygnoo _ _ _ _ _ _ _ _ _ _ the order in which things
                         3   happen

4. susenc   _ _ _ _ _ _   a count of the people who
                       4   live in a place

5. tegalede   _ _ _ _ _ _ _ _   a person chosen to speak
                        5   for a group

6. yrrfe   _ _ _ _ _   a boat that carries people
                     6   and goods across water

7. ecatr   _ _ _ _ _   a trail in the forest made
                      7   by animals

8. Mystery Word: _ _ _ _ _ _ _
                     1 2 3 4 5 6 7

Name _____ Date _____

Underground Railroad Journey

Look at the map of the Underground Railroad in Indiana. The map shows some of the stops in Indiana that led to freedom. Use the map to plan an escape from Kentucky to Canada. List the cities along your chosen route. Then answer the question.

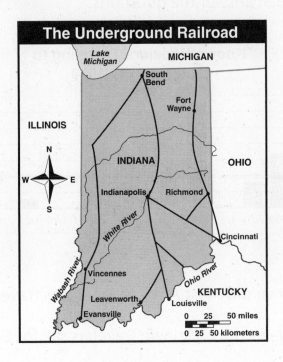

The Underground Railroad

ESCAPE PLAN		
first stop: _____	second stop: _____	third stop: _____
fourth stop: _____	fifth stop: _____	sixth stop: _____

1. Why do you think traveling through Indiana was dangerous for those escaping from slavery? _____

_____

Name _____   Date _____

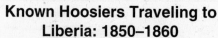

Liberia Travelers Bar Graph

The bar graph below shows the number of known African Americans from Indiana who traveled to Liberia, Africa, from 1850 to 1860. Look at the bar graph. Then answer the questions.

Known Hoosiers Traveling to Liberia: 1850–1860

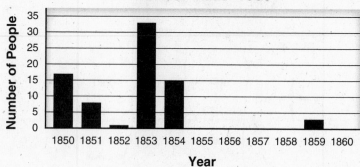

1. In which year did most African Americans travel to Liberia? _____

2. In which years did no known travelers sail for Liberia? _____

3. How many people traveled to Liberia in 1859? _____

4. Would you predict that more or less people might travel to Liberia after 1860? Why? _____

Design a Civil War Memorial

Create a memorial for those in Indiana who fought or helped others during the Civil War. Choose your subject from the list below. Then answer the questions.

The Iron Brigade	Benjamin Harrison	Mary Wise
Lovina Streight	Mary Ann Shadd Cary	The Fighting 28th

1. What did you choose as the subject of your memorial? Why? _____

_____

_____

2. How did you decide to portray, or show, your subject? _____

_____

The Freedmen's Bureau Organizer

Fill in the circles with services that the Freedmen's Bureau provided to African Americans during Reconstruction. Then answer the questions.

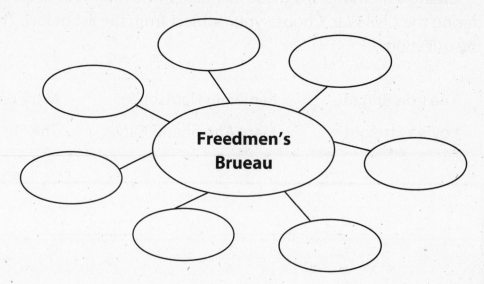

Freedmen's Brueau

1. Why do you think that the Freedmen's Bureau needed to provide these services to African Americans? _____

_____

2. Which services might someone need immediately? Why? _____

_____

3. How do you think that going to a school run by the Freedmen's Bureau after the Civil War might compare to going to school today? _____

_____

CURRICULUM CONNECTION ART

CURRICULUM CONNECTION LANGUAGE ARTS

A Farmer's Catalog

Create two pages for a farm catalog. Choose a category for each page, such as farm tools or household items. Include things for sale that a farmer living in the late 1800s might need to buy. Describe and draw a picture of each item. Include a number for your item and a price. Then answer the question below.

THE FARMER'S CATALOG	THE FARMER'S CATALOG
Category: _____	Category: _____
Description:	Description:
Item #:	Item #:
Price:	Price:

Why were catalogues important for Indiana's farmers who lived during the 1800s? _____

_____

Name _____   Date _____

Causes of City Growth

Fill in the chart to show why Indiana's cities grew. Then answer the questions.

Growth of Indiana Cities	
better transportation	
new forms of communication	
factories were built	
increase in population	

1. How did railroads help cities to become a center of industry? _____

_____

2. What products did two major South Bend factories make in the 1800s?

_____

Name _____ Date _____

Population Map: 1860

Look at the map of Indiana's population in 1860. Then answer the questions.

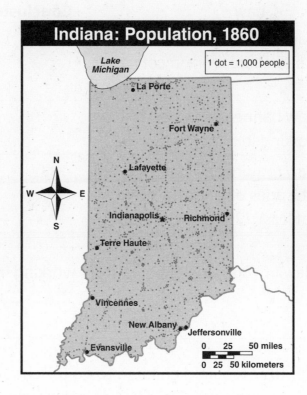

1. How many people does one dot represent?

_____

2. Which area had a larger population, the northwest or southeast?

_____

Child Labor Laws

Look at the child labor laws that Indiana passed from 1867 to 1897. Why do you think these laws needed to be passed? Why were the laws necessary? Write your conclusions below. Then answer the questions.

Law	Conclusions About the Law
In 1867 a law limited the number of hours children could work in cotton factories.	
In 1879 a law banned boys under 14 from working in mines.	
In 1897 a law required all children between the ages of 8 and 14 to go to school at least 12 weeks per year.	

1. Did the law in 1867 stop children from working in factories? How do you know? _____

_____

2. The law in 1897 required children to go to school for 12 weeks. About how many months was this? How does this compare to how many months you must go to school? _____

_____

Vocabulary Review

Read the words below each line. Write a word from the box that belongs with the two words. Then write a sentence using that word.

plantation	technology	discrimination
reaper	industry	union

Word   **Sentence**

1. _____   _____
   unfair   unequal   _____

2. _____   _____
   tools   skill   _____

3. _____   _____
   business   service   _____

4. _____   _____
   cutter   machine   _____

5. _____   _____
   farm   land   _____

6. _____   _____
   group   workers   _____

CURRICULUM CONNECTION ART

CURRICULUM CONNECTION LANGUAGE ARTS

Invitation to Invention

Choose an invention from the chart below. Then write an invitation to celebrate the invention. Fill in the time and date of the celebration. Decide where the celebration will be held. Explain to guests why the invention is important. Decorate the invitation with a design or a picture of the invention.

INVENTION	INVENTOR	YEAR INVENTED
telephone	Alexander Graham Bell	1876
long lasting electric light	Thomas Alva Edison	1879
electric railroad system	Frank Julian Sprague	1887
gasoline powered car	Frank and Charles Edgar Duryea	1893
first successful airplane	Wilbur and Orville Wright	1903

A SPECIAL INVITATION TO CELEBRATE
THE INVENTION OF _____

When: _____

Where: _____

Why: _____

Suffrage Signs

Look at the picture below of women marching for voting rights. Fill in the empty signs in the picture with slogans that call for the right to vote. Then answer the questions.

1. Do you think that it took courage for women to protest for voting rights?

Why or why not? _____

_____

2. Why do you think that it took so long for women to get the right to vote?

_____

_____

3. How did May Wright Sewell and Ida Husted Harper help women to get

suffrage? _____

_____

_____

Indiana's Beaches Graph

Indiana's beaches along Lake Michigan are sometimes closed because the water is not always clean. State officials also give out warnings when the water is unclean. Use the line graph to answer the questions.

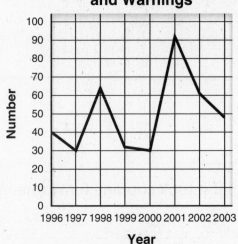

Lake Michigan Beach Closings and Warnings

1. What does the line graph show? _____

2. Which year had the most beach closings and warnings? _____

3. Which two years had the fewest beach closings and warnings? _____

_____

4. What prediction might you make about beach closings and warnings for

the years not shown on the graph? _____

_____

Name _____ Date _____

A Poem About Hard Times

Many Americans suffered during the Great Depression. Write a poem about one of the subjects below. Then answer the questions.

the stock market crash of 1929	losing a job	standing on a soup line
losing a home or farm	Hoovervilles	the Dust Bowl

1. How did the stock market crash affect businesses and workers? _____

_____

2. Why were "Hoovervilles" named after President Herbert Hoover? _____

_____

3. What happened to many farm families who lived in the Dust Bowl? _____

_____

Name _____ Date _____

During the Depression Map

Look at the map below. Then answer the questions.

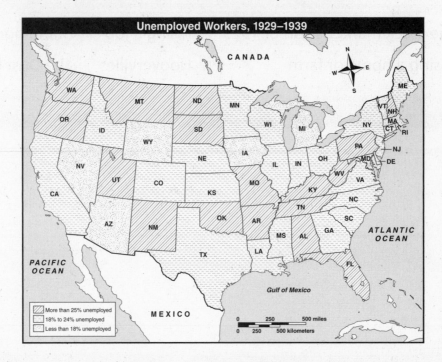

1. Which states had the lowest percentage of unemployed workers? _____

_____

2. Were the states with the lowest percentage of unemployed workers in

the northern or southern part of the United States? _____

3. What was the percentage of unemployed workers in Indiana? _____

4. How did the percentage of unemployed workers in Indiana compare to

other states? _____

Civil Rights Dictionary

Create dictionary pages for the Civil Rights era. Look at the entries below. Write a sentence or two about each person.

A Civil Rights Dictionary

Robert Brokenburr _____

_____
_____
_____
_____
_____

Richard Hatcher _____

_____
_____
_____
_____

Robert Kennedy _____

_____
_____
_____
_____
_____

Martin Luther King, Jr. _____

_____
_____
_____
_____

Henry Richardson _____

_____
_____
_____

Radio News Bulletin

Create a radio news bulletin about the Cuban Missile Crisis. Let your listeners know what the conflict is about. Use the information from page 212 in your textbook to help you write your announcement.

RADIO ANNOUNCEMENT

Date: October, 1962
Place: Cuba

We interrupt this program to bring you a special news bulletin!

_____

_____

_____

_____

_____

_____

_____

_____

_____

_____

_____

Name _____   Date _____

A Soldier's Medal

Create a medal of honor for soldiers fighting in the War on Terrorism. Then answer the questions.

1. Why did the United States and its allies invade Afghanistan? _____

_____

2. Why did the United States and its allies invade Iraq? _____

_____

3. What is one way that the Indiana Department of Homeland Security

prepares to help Hoosiers in case of a disaster? _____

_____

Vocabulary Review

Choose a vocabulary word from the box that best solves each clue. Then unscramble the circled letters to make a word that answers the question at the bottom of the page.

invention	decade	drought	protests
satellites	truce	dictator	rationing

1. The Dust Bowl had one. _ _ _○_ _○_

2. Space has these. ○_ _ _ _ _ _ _○_

3. An airplane is one. _ _ ○_ _ _○_

4. Every ten years is one. _ _ _ _ _ ○_

5. Migrant farm workers had these. ○_ _ _○_ _ _

6. During World War II, Hoosiers lived with this. ○_ _ _ _○_ _ _

7. Adolf Hitler was one. _ _ _ _ _ _ ○_

8. North and South Korea signed one of these. _○_ _ _

9. Who starts up new businesses?

_ _ _ _ _ _ _ _ _ _ _ _

Government Voicemail

Create a voicemail greeting for people calling our government. Explain to listeners what each branch of government does. Use the form below to write your greeting.

Hello. You have reached the United States Government. Listen to the instructions below to leave your message.

For the Executive Branch, press 1. This branch of government _____

_____

_____

For the Legislative Branch, press 2. This branch of government _____

_____

_____

For the Judicial Branch, press 3. This branch of government _____

_____

_____

Governor Appointment List

Fill in the list of jobs that the Governor of Indiana has the power to appoint. Then answer the questions.

Appointment List

1. Appoints the heads of state departments, such as _____.

2. Appoints _____ justices to the Judicial Branch.

3. Appoints a _____ to the Office of Management and Budget.

---

4. Who elects our governor? _____

_____

5. How long is one term of service for our governor? _____

_____

6. In what branch of government does our governor work? _____

_____

7. What are some of the duties of our Lieutenant Governor? _____

_____

Use with Unit 6, Chart and Graph Skills

CURRICULUM CONNECTION **LANGUAGE ARTS**

Court of Appeals Flow Chart

Indiana's Court of Appeals is our state's second highest court. Look at the flow chart to learn about how Indiana's Court of Appeals works.

1. People can ask judges on Indiana's Court of Appeals to change a decision about a case made by another court.

2. Each side is given 20 to 30 minutes to present their viewpoints. The judges may ask questions.

3. The judges meet to decide the case. This may take many months to reach.

4. The judges present their decision.

1. Why might someone bring a case to the Court of Appeals? _____

_____

2. Does each side tell their viewpoints out loud before or after the judges review the case?

_____

3. For how many minutes can each side present their viewpoints out loud?

_____

_____

Name _____   Date _____

Government Fact Sheet

Make a fact sheet about the duties of local government. Fill in three duties of county governments and municipal governments. Then complete the sentences below.

GOVERNMENT FACT SHEET	
COUNTY DUTIES	**MUNICIPAL DUTIES**
1.	1.
2.	2.
3.	3.

1. One thing that city workers do is _____

_____.

2. One thing that townships do is _____

_____.

CURRICULUM CONNECTION LANGUAGE ARTS

CURRICULUM CONNECTION MATH

Supply and Demand Shopping

When there is a good supply of an item in a store, you can shop for the lowest price. Imagine that you need to buy the following: 1 pair of Star Sneakers, 1 Air Backpack, and 1 pair of Sunny Sunglasses. Look at the three advertisements to find the lowest prices. Then fill in the chart below. Finally, answer the questions.

Nick's Sporting Goods
"We have it all at Nicks!"
Star Sneakers: $75
Air Backpack: $25
Sunny Sunglasses: $15

Super Sports
"A super place to shop!"
Star Sneakers: Out of stock
Air Backpack: $25
Sunny Sunglasses: $10

Family Sports
"Fun for the whole family!"
Star Sneakers: Coming soon!
Air Backpack: $25
Sunny Sunglasses: $12

ITEM	LOWEST PRICE	STORE WITH LOWEST PRICE

1. Which item has a lower supply than demand for it? How can you tell? (Hint: Prices often increase when demand is high and supply is low.)

   _____

2. Which item has a greater supply than demand for it? How can you tell? (Hint: Prices often decrease when a supply is high and demand is low.)

   _____

"The Crossroads of America" Brochure

Make a brochure to attract businesses to Indiana. Explain why Indiana's transportation systems are good for businesses. Draw a picture on the brochure.

Come to Indiana: "The Crossroads of America" Highways Railways	Air Travel Waterway

Use with Unit 6, Map and Globe Skills

Indiana Road Map Trip

Look at the map of the Evansville area. Color the interstate highways blue, the U.S. highways red, and the state highways purple. Then plan three routes from Evansville to Angel Mounds State Historic Site following the directions below.

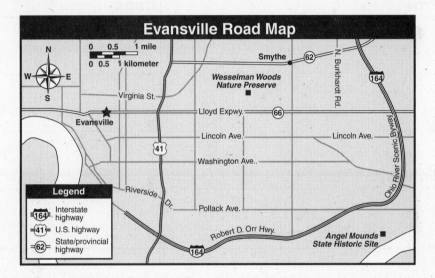

1. What route could you take to get from Evansville to the Angel Mounds Site using mostly highways? _____

_____

2. What route could you take to get from Evansville to the Angel Mounds Site without using U.S. highways? _____

_____

3. What route could you take to get from Evansville to the Angel Mounds Site using mostly state highways? _____

_____

Name _____ Date _____

Pros and Cons List

Think about the positive and negative effects of globalization. Write three positive effects in the *Pros* column and three negative effects in the *Cons* column. Then answer the question.

Pros	Cons
1. _____	1. _____
2. _____	2. _____
3. _____	3. _____

Do you think that globalization is good for Indiana? Why or why not?

_____

_____

_____

_____

_____

_____

_____

_____

A Memo to Businesses

Complete the memo to owners of industries in Indiana. Fill in your name and the date on the memo. Use the terms in the box to write the memo.

conservation	wind	recycling	fossil fuels	ethanol
global warming	acid rain	sun	weather	

TO: Indiana's Industries   SUBJECT: Environmental Challenges
FROM: _____   DATE: _____

Please note the following challenges that Indiana is now facing.

- Burning _____ is polluting the air, making it dangerous to breathe.

- Chemicals from factories and cars are dissolving in rainwater to form _____.

- Some scientists think pollution is causing _____, or a rise in temperature that might cause extreme _____ conditions.

Here are some things we can do to fix these problems.

- We can reduce pollution through _____.

- We can reuse materials and save natural resources by _____.

- Some scientists think we can help to stop warming temperatures by using different kinds of energy sources. One idea is to use energy from the _____ by putting huge panels in space. Another idea is to use new fuels, such as _____. We might also use energy from the _____ with huge windmills.

We look forward to your cooperation in these matters.

Vocabulary Review

Read the definitions below. Complete the puzzle with the vocabulary word that matches the definition.

Across

1. things that are sold or traded to another country
2. a course you take to get somewhere
3. the protection and careful use of natural resources
4. money left over after a business pays its expenses
5. a plan for using money

Down

6. producing a few products instead of many
7. respect and loyal support of one's country
8. the last word of NAFTA
9. the head of a municipal government
10. a tax on goods brought into a country